EQUAL TO EVERYTHING

Judge Brenda
and the
Supreme Court

Afua Hirsch   Henny Beaumont

In a beautiful town in Yorkshire, where a castle still stands tall
Class 3 ended their holidays and headed back to school.

Chatting about trips to the seaside and all the summer's fun,
one little girl stood quietly. She didn't yet know anyone.

New to Richmond, Yorkshire, Ama was finding her way around
when Miss Evans announced their topic,
"the landmarks of London town."
Ama came alive: statues and skyscrapers everywhere
"What's that?" she asked, "on the edge of Parliament Square."

"That's our Supreme Court,
where twelve judges have work to do,
led by a woman called Brenda Hale,
who's from Richmond just like you!"

"Judges like on the telly?" asked Henry.
"Giving dancing scores?"
"No," said Miss Evans laughing,
"ones that decide our laws.

Class 3, we'll be visiting London soon, you've given me a thought,
when we go to see the landmarks – let's visit the Supreme Court!"

When Mum picked her up at three,
Ama was full of the news of the term,
listing new friends she'd made,
and London landmarks she would learn.
When she mentioned the Supreme Court,
and its president, Lady Hale,
Mum smiled and said, "wait till we get home
and I'll tell you my tale."

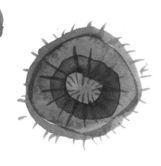

Ama's mum was a dinner lady,
who worked at the school in town
where they lived before, in St Helen's,
she was well known all around

for her delicious food: her fine, fresh fish,
her crunchy, crispy chips,
fresh veggies, cakes and crumbles
that thrilled the kids to bits.

At home, Mum started the story,
as they both sat down to tea.
"I work very hard at my job,
but do you know what happened to me?

My friends and I found out that men,
who were doing the same work,
were getting paid more than us women,
which made us feel very hurt."

"Boys are naughty mummy!" said Ama,
"Henry makes Miss Evans go red."
"Well girls aren't always perfect," smiled Mum,
amused by what Ama said.

"There are lots of men who work hard, like your Dad,
who we miss every day."
Ama and Mum looked at Dad's photo,
as they always did since he passed away.
"Your Dad and I made a brilliant team when pay wasn't equal or fair.
Lady Hale helped us change the law so women could get their share."

"Do you know Lady Hale?" asked Ama, "have you met her? Tell me more!"
"She's so inspiring!" said Mum, "higher than any woman judge before."

A few weeks later, in Autumn term, leaves falling from the trees,
Class 3 set off to London, to all the sights they planned to see:
the London Eye, St Paul's Cathedral, memorials to past wars fought,
and finally, to Ama's delight, a tour of the Supreme Court!

COURAGE
CALLS TO
COURAGE
EVERYWHERE

Class 3 gazed at the courtrooms:
colourful carpets and lamps aglow.
At the front, a curved wooden table
where the judges all sit in a row.

The library, with thousands of books,
bigger than Ama had ever seen
and an exhibition of the Court's history
and a sculpture of the Queen.

At lunchtime the hungry children
skipped to the court cafe to eat
and Miss Evans told them the time
had come for a very special treat.
"Yes! Chocolate cake!" yelled Henry,
standing up and licking his lips.
"Not that kind of treat Henry,"
Miss Evans sighed,
with hands upon her hips.

Just then a kind-looking lady walked in, lifting Miss Evans' frown.
It was Lady Hale herself! come to meet the kids from her home town.
The children had heard so much of her and the decisions that she makes,
meeting her *in real life* was even better than chocolate cake!

"When I was little," Lady Hale explained,
"my parents taught children like you.
I worked as hard as I could at school,
there was so much
I wanted to do!

I learned about past
kings and queens,
their bad deeds and their wars;
the people who stood up to them,
and how it changed our laws."

"Was there anything you weren't good at?" asked Julian,
sticking up his hand.
"I wasn't sporty," Lady Hale laughed,
"and my artwork wasn't that grand!
But I was interested in
justice and I noticed
when things
weren't fair.

At university out of one hundred students,
guess how many girls were there?"

Jazzy thought for a moment, then "half one hundred is fifty!" she said.
"Well done," said Lady Hale, "that would be fair, Jazzy,
but actually instead,
there were only six of us and when I decided that law was what I'd do,
people said women weren't good lawyers,
and *that's* why there were so few!"

THE CHILDREN ACT

"Did you believe them?" Oriane asked,
"did you think that was the cause?"
"No!" said Lady Hale. "*I* became a lawyer
and I wrote new laws,
including the Children Act that says
when adults row
it's children's health and happiness
that matters most now."

"Everyone *knows* it's important we're happy!" Matilda blurted out loud.
"I agree!" laughed Lady Hale, "I'm a mum myself
and of that I'm very proud.
But sadly, adults do argue
and you can get caught in the fight.
Things can be complicated,
not all answers are
black and white."

"What do you mean?" asked Roxy, "we know what's right and wrong!"
"I'll tell you a story," said Lady Hale, "to help you follow along.

There was a mum from Tanzania, her children were British like you.
When she asked to stay in this country, what she said wasn't always true.

She was told she would be sent away. Her family was terribly sad.
Her kids would've had to go with her,
leaving their friends
and even their Dad!

But we changed the law by
deciding it wasn't fair to
make her leave.
Children shouldn't suffer for
adults' mistakes.
That is what I believe."

"Do you always give children what they want,"
asked Max, raising his hand.

"Not always," answered Lady Hale.
"Sometimes the law of the land
means we have to be strict with parents,
like the dad who wanted to know
if his child could miss school for Disney World,
to that I had to say no."

"But Lady Hale!" asked Eli, worried, "Will you stop us going on holiday?"
"No," laughed Lady Hale, "but if you were off school,
you'd have missed this trip today."

The children looked at each other
with Disney World in their thoughts
but agreed it would've been very sad to miss the Supreme Court.

"Is all your work about children?"
Anoushka's shyness slipped away.
"No," said Lady Hale. "In one case,
a lady, famous
for ballet,

now old, needed help at night to get up and go to the loo.
But the council said she should wear nappies
when she needed to do a poo!"

"I thought that
wasn't fair at all.
You wouldn't like that,
would you?"
"Oh no," said the children,
giggling, "what a horrible
thing to do."

"It was very sad" said Brenda, "of five judges, only I agreed.
So the dancer who'd asked for help lost her case, and remained in need."

"So judges argue with each other,
like when my friends disagree?"
asked Eva as Lady Hale listened to Class 3 patiently.

"Well, it's our job to think carefully, then say what we think is right.
So when we don't agree, it's not the same as having a fight."

"I've seen women held back by unfairness,
in their lives and their careers,
I was the first woman on this court,
the only one for many years.
I see things a bit differently, and I'm not afraid to say,
if more girls become judges, the law will improve along the way."

"Can't people see girls are as good as boys?"
Diana plucked up the courage to ask,
"Good question," said Brenda
"many do see it now,
but it's been a difficult task."

"Boys are our friends," said Ama.
"Class 3 boys are on our side!
And so was my Dad. I miss him so much
ever since he died."
Lady Hale put her arm around Ama,
and said from the heart she knew
how hard it was to lose your dad,
she lost hers as a child too.

Hearing about Judge Brenda's story helped soothe Ama's worries away.
"Lady Hale, you helped my Mum
when she went to court about unfair pay."

Lady Hale's eyes sparkled. "Well Ama, that case gave us a choice!
By fighting that injustice, your Mum gave all women a voice."

Time for one last question, from Spencer
"do you wear funny clothes, sometimes?"
"Well, there are many symbols," said Lady Hale
"some are quite sublime!

The gown and floppy black hat
you see on display is rarely seen.
They're used for special occasions,
like when Parliament's
opened by the Queen."

"Class 3, legal landmarks are some of the best landmarks of all!
And what I've learned in my life is, work hard as you can at school.
Always follow your dreams, ignore anyone who tries to cut you short,

Because you are equal to everything: even a judge at the
Supreme Court!"

For more curious readers

Ama is a fictional character but Judge Brenda, the Supreme Court, and all the cases she tells the children about, are real.

Ama's home town of Richmond, is where Brenda Hale, the first ever woman to be a judge in the Supreme Court in the UK, grew up.

Brenda had to do well in an exam to get into her secondary school, and although she was successful, there were only half the number of grammar school places for girls as for boys. This was the first time that Brenda noticed that girls and boys did not always have the same opportunities.

Brenda (4) with her sisters Frances (3) and Jill (12)

She had a similar experience at university. She was one of only six women and around one hundred men on her course.

Brenda did so well at Cambridge University she finished top of the class, and started training to be a lawyer. At that time there were still very few women lawyers – women were only allowed to become lawyers in 1919. Today just as many women become lawyers as men, but not as many women become judges, especially top judges like Brenda.

Brenda as Kate in the Yeomen of the Guard, Cambridge 1966

Brenda at home in Derbyshire with her daughter Julia (2)

Brenda did not become a judge straight away. She taught law at a University and wrote books on it. She then went on to help make laws, and also became a mum. She was the first woman ever to become a Law Commissioner. Law Commissioners propose new laws for Parliament to approve.

One of the laws Brenda helped to write is the Children Act 1989. The Children Act makes sure that whenever decisions are made about a child, the child comes first. The law says that if a child is not safe, an adult must step in to protect them. The Children Act has been copied around the world.

After the Law Commission, Brenda became a judge. Judges listen to two sides of a story and have to decide what is fair. The law says people cannot be treated unfairly because of where they were born, their disability, their age, the colour of their skin, their religious beliefs, who they love or whether they are a boy or a girl. The law is there to protect everyone from unfair treatment.

Brenda worked in lots of different types of courts before she became a Supreme Court judge. Judges sit in many courts around the country and decide lots of different types of cases. Some are about a person accused of committing a crime, others are about what happens to families, people in hospital, businesses and all sorts of other situations where people disagree about what should happen.

Brenda sworn in as a High Court Judge, 1994, with husband Julian and daughter Julia

Most courts only have one judge. If a person believes that a judge has made the wrong decision, it may be possible to appeal it to a higher court. The higher the court, the more judges there are likely to be deciding one case. Sometimes the law is not clear and judges have to make decisions to set the law.

Brenda remained the only woman judge in the Supreme Court until 2017 when she was joined by Lady Black. In 2018, Lady Arden joined the Court, bringing the total number of women judges to three out of the twelve.

The Supreme Court is the highest court in the United Kingdom. Sometimes decisions of the Supreme Court can be taken to the European Court of Human Rights in Strasbourg in France.

Brenda has said that the law is supposed to be about justice, fairness and equality. This means the law is for everybody. Part of being fair and equal, Brenda

has pointed out, is looking fair and equal, with women and people from different backgrounds visible on the court, the same as in our communities.

The Supreme Court was the first court in the UK to have every case live on the internet and is open to the public, so that people – just like the children in Class 3 – can go and look around.

Although the judges of the Supreme Court have black and gold robes for special occasions, they do not wear any fancy costumes or wigs, as judges and lawyers still do in criminal courts. All their decisions are written down and put on the Supreme Court's website for all to see. The judges don't always make decisions in the court building in London – they sometimes travel to other cities.

Brenda with fellow Supreme Court Justices, 2019

What did you think? We would love to hear what you
thought about the story of Judge Brenda,
Email judgebrenda@lag.org.uk
Noticing things is an important part of being a good judge.

 Did you notice the little frogs in Ama's story?

For M, B, B, K and S. – HB

To my grandfather PK who dreamed of being a lawyer.
To my mother Mary and father Peter who gave me the confidence to become one.
To my daughter Naya who inspired this book (especially the cheeky bits).
And for all children who have a dream. – AF

Legal Action Group would like to thank the Sigrid Rausing Trust and
our friends and supporters for funding this publication.
We are incredibly grateful to Brenda Hale for her support and
encouragement and for giving her time so willingly during
the production of this book. Thank you to Roxy Lang who
came up with the idea for this book.

the access to
justice charity

Legal Action Group (LAG) is a national
charity committed to improving access
to justice. LAG promotes equal access to
justice as a fundamental democratic right:
www.lag.org.uk.

This edition published in Great Britain 2019
by LAG Education and Service Trust Limited
National Pro Bono Centre, 48 Chancery Lane, London WC2A 1JF
www.lag.org.uk

© Legal Action Group 2019
Illustrations © Henny Beaumont 2019

Book design: Sarah Finan

British Library Cataloguing in Publication Data
a CIP catalogue record for this book is available from the British Library.

ISBN 978 1 912273 48 5

Printed in China